singing time!

grade 2

Step by step instructions for
ABRSM and other singing exams

David Turnbull

© Copyright 2001 by Bosworth & Co. Limited, London

BOSWORTH 14-15 Berners Street, London, W1T 3LJ

D0314075

Singing Time! Grade 2

To the Pupil

Almost everyone can sing. Singing brings pleasure to the singer – and often to the listener! It is perhaps the best way to learn about music. Your health will improve, too, because singing involves good breathing and muscle control. You don't have to buy a voice – you have one built in.

This book will help you to make the most of your natural singing gift. The songs in it provide you with a collection of music on which you can build.

Good singers don't just learn songs by ear. They must also learn how to sing at sight, so that they can learn new music quickly, and join singing groups. To do this, singers must understand the way music is written down. Knowing about rhythm, pitch, keys and intervals is just as important to singers as it is to instrumentalists.

You can learn a lot about singing from books like this, but you will learn much more if you also have a good teacher, and listen to experienced singers.

If you want to know more detail about music theory, you can use books in the *Theory Time!* series. References are given in the text. Practice for aural tests can be found in *Aural Time! Grade 2*. These books, by the same author, are all published by Bosworth.

To the Teacher

This book contains enough material for Grade 2 ABRSM Singing (2001–2002 syllabus). Much of the material may also be used for the Initial Grade of the ABRSM Choral Singing syllabus, and teachers may also consider making use of this examination for groups of their singing pupils. Some introductory material is included in Part 7.

Examination regulations provide that *any* printed edition of a song is acceptable, and that songs may be transposed to any key to suit the voice of the performer.

All the examinations include sight singing, and this important aspect of a singer's equipment is stressed. The necessary theoretical background found in *Singing Time! Grade 1* is extended in this book. Songs are grouped by key, as without a knowledge of scales and keys no skill in sight singing can be achieved.

In Grade 2, **one** song must be chosen from **each** of the lists A, B and C. **The total performance time of these songs must not exceed five minutes**. In addition, one traditional song must be offered, of the candidate's own choice. **All songs must be sung from memory.**

Songs included from List A are: *A-roving, The Oak And The Ash* and *Cockles And Mussels*. From List B are *Morning Has Broken,* the *Coventry Carol* and Schumann's *Butterfly*. From List C are *Little Spanish Town* and *London Birds*.

All other songs are traditional, any one of which may be offered in the traditional song section of the examination. Chord indications are included to help *in practice only*.

Further help with theory can be found in the author's books in the *Theory Time!* series, and with aural tests in the author's *Aural Time! Grade 2*. All these books are published by Bosworth.

David Turnbull

Part I

Warming up

Use these exercises to warm up each time you practise.

1 Breath control

Count to four in each bar at first, then to six, then to eight.

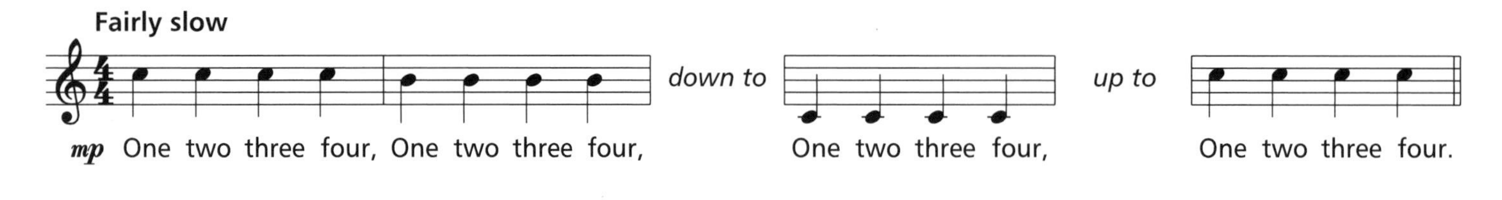

2 Vowel practice

Sing this first to 'noo', then 'nor', then 'nah', then 'nee'.

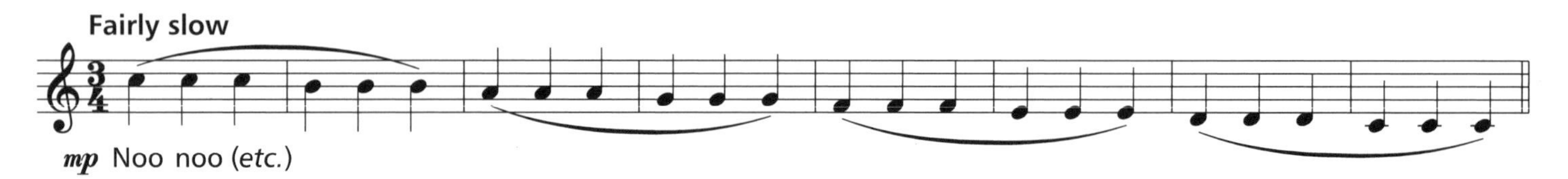

3 Control of dynamics

Sing this downward scale getting quieter all the time.

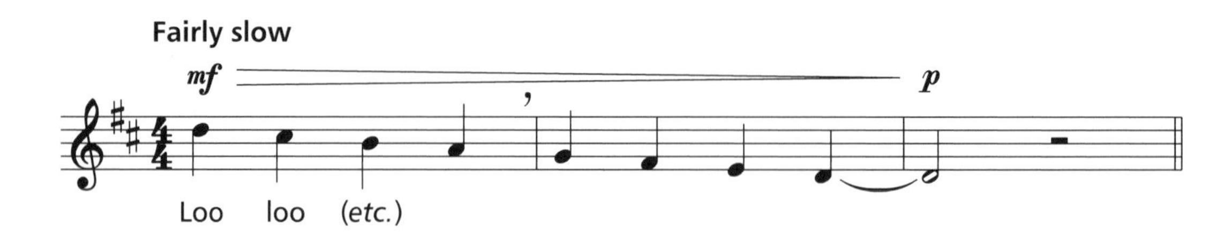

1. Sing this first to 'loo', then 'lah', then 'leh'.
2. At first, take a breath at the end of bar 1.
3. Then sing it a little faster, but all in one breath.

4 Arpeggios

Sing some upward arpeggios, to help extend your range.

St Paul's Steeple makes an excellent warm-up exercise. Sing it first starting on C. Then sing it starting on D flat, then D, then E flat, then E.

Listen carefully to the sound of the vowels, and make the consonants crisp. Breathe after each comma and don't forget the dynamics.

St Paul's Steeple

English Traditional (adapted)

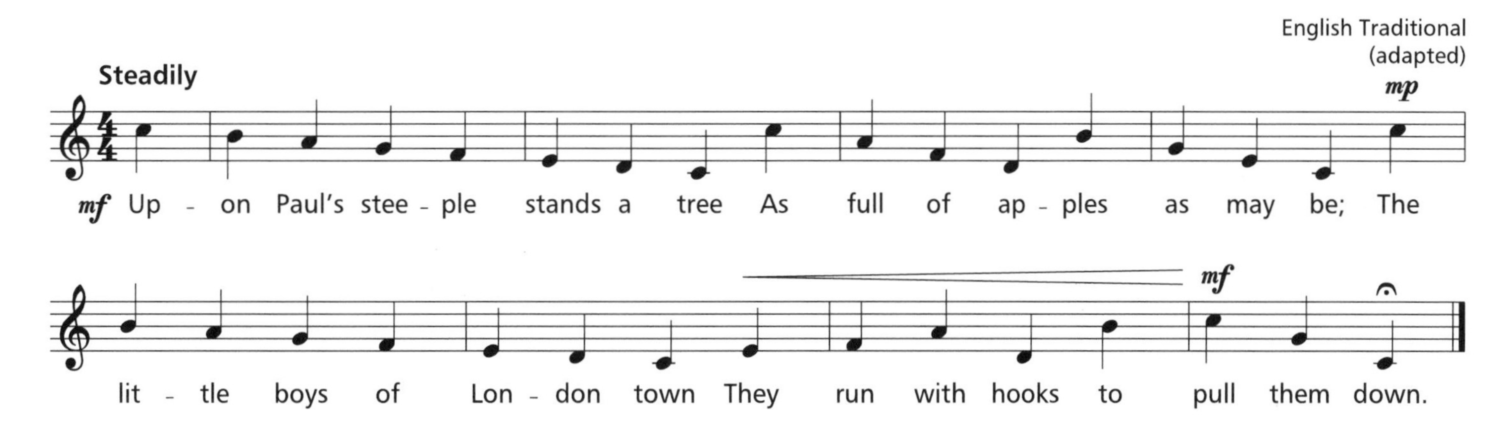

Some revision

Keys and key signatures

Make sure you know in which key a song is written.

St Paul's Steeple is in the key of C major, which has no sharps or flats. All other major keys need either sharps or flats, shown by their **key signatures**.

Revise the major key signatures explained in *Singing Time! Grade 1*:

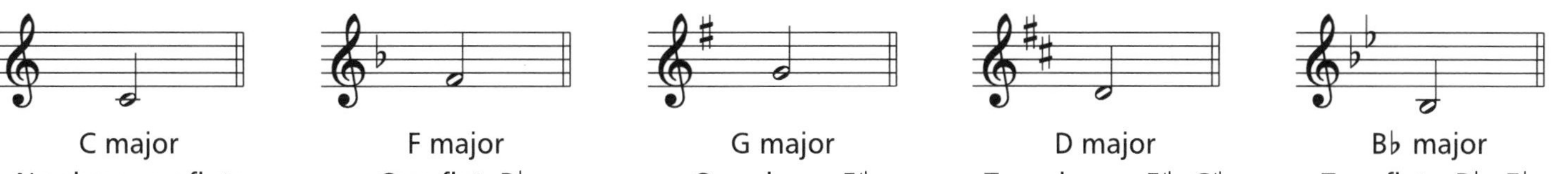

C major
No sharps or flats

F major
One flat: B♭

G major
One sharp: F♯

D major
Two sharps: F♯, C♯

B♭ major
Two flats: B♭, E♭

New keys are explained later in this book.

Intervals

When practising a new song, look carefully at the intervals between the notes. The first eight notes of *St Paul's Steeple* are each a single step apart. Between 'tree' and 'As' there is an upward jump of an octave. Between 'As' and 'full' there is a downward jump of a third, and so on.

Memorising intervals

Many people do this by remembering the starts of songs. Here are some suggestions, but make your own collection, and write them down on the music paper on page 46.

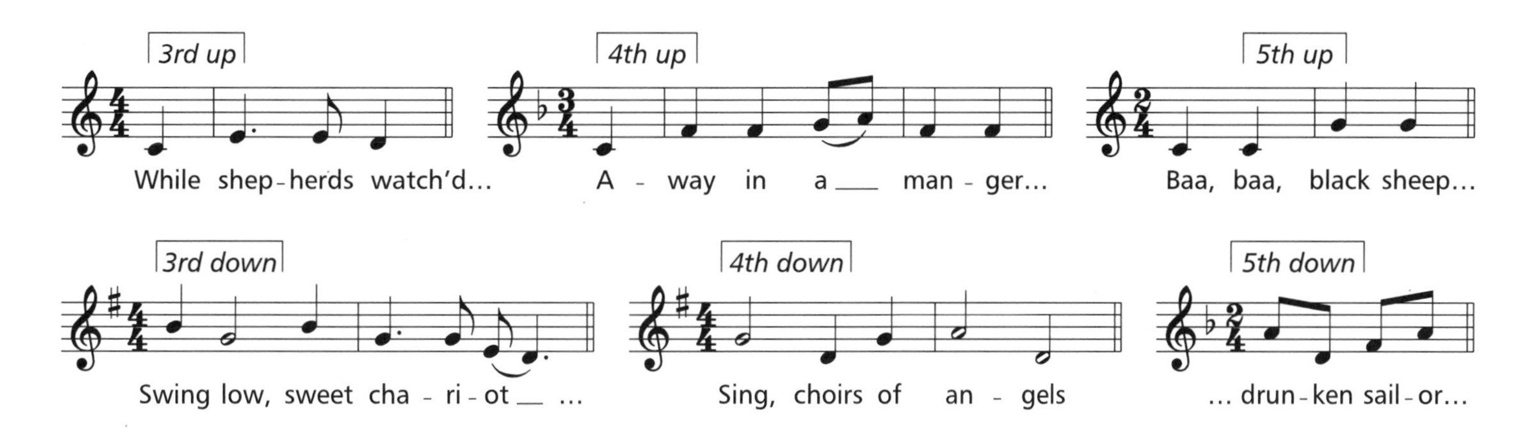

Part 2

Songs in F major

1 Songs with minim beats

In *Singing Time! Grade 1*, songs were counted in main beats which were either crotchets ($\frac{2}{4}$, $\frac{3}{4}$ and $\frac{4}{4}$ times), quavers ($\frac{3}{8}$ time), or dotted crotchets ($\frac{6}{8}$ time).

Some songs are counted in **minim** beats. If the time signature has 2 as its lower figure, the beats are minims. For example, $\frac{2}{2}$ means two minim beats to the bar.

When a minim is worth one beat, a crotchet is worth half a beat, and a semibreve two beats, as in this song in F major.

Blow Away The Morning Dew

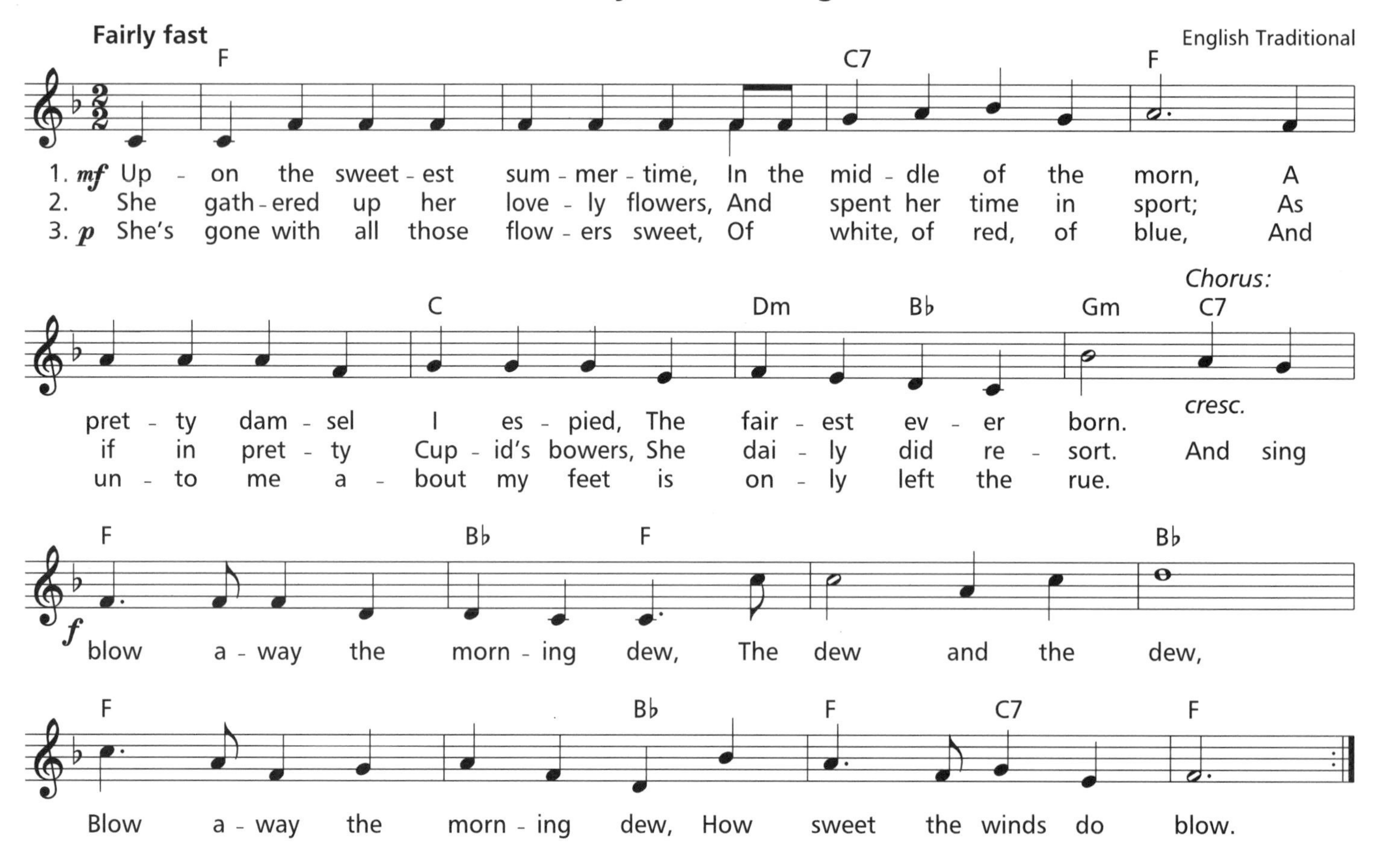

2 Beating time

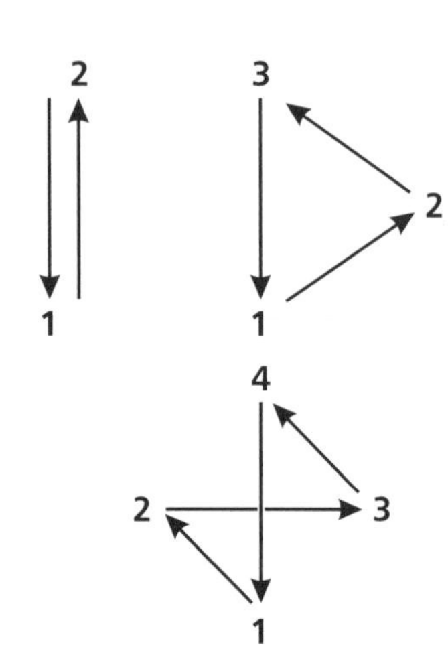

Conductors beat time when conducting choirs. You too will find it useful to be able to do this – if you beat time while you are practising a song it will help your sense of rhythm.

Here are the conducting patterns for two-, three- and four- beat times.

- Two-time is 'down-up'.
- Three-time is a triangle, with the second beat going out to your right.
- Four-time is beaten as a square, with the second beat going to your left, and the third beat to your right.

Practise these patterns with a loose wrist, letting the wrist do most of the work.

When The Saints Go Marching In

3 Syncopation

Notice that bar 3 above has an unusual rhythm. The setting of the word 'pilgrim' hides the two minim beats of the bar.

When notes fall on unexpected beats, the rhythm is said to be *syncopated*.

Counting and clapping

When learning a new song, work out the rhythm of the notes very carefully.

- Choose a slow tempo.
- Count the beats of each bar aloud, like this.
- Clap the rhythm of the notes as you count.
- Then sing the notes in rhythm.

A-roving is one of the set choices for Grade 2, and is in 2/2 time.

A-roving

A-roving doesn't start on the key-note, F, but on the C below it. Songs starting with an incomplete bar often start on a note other than the key-note.

Early One Morning is a fine song, and also a useful exercise to extend your range.

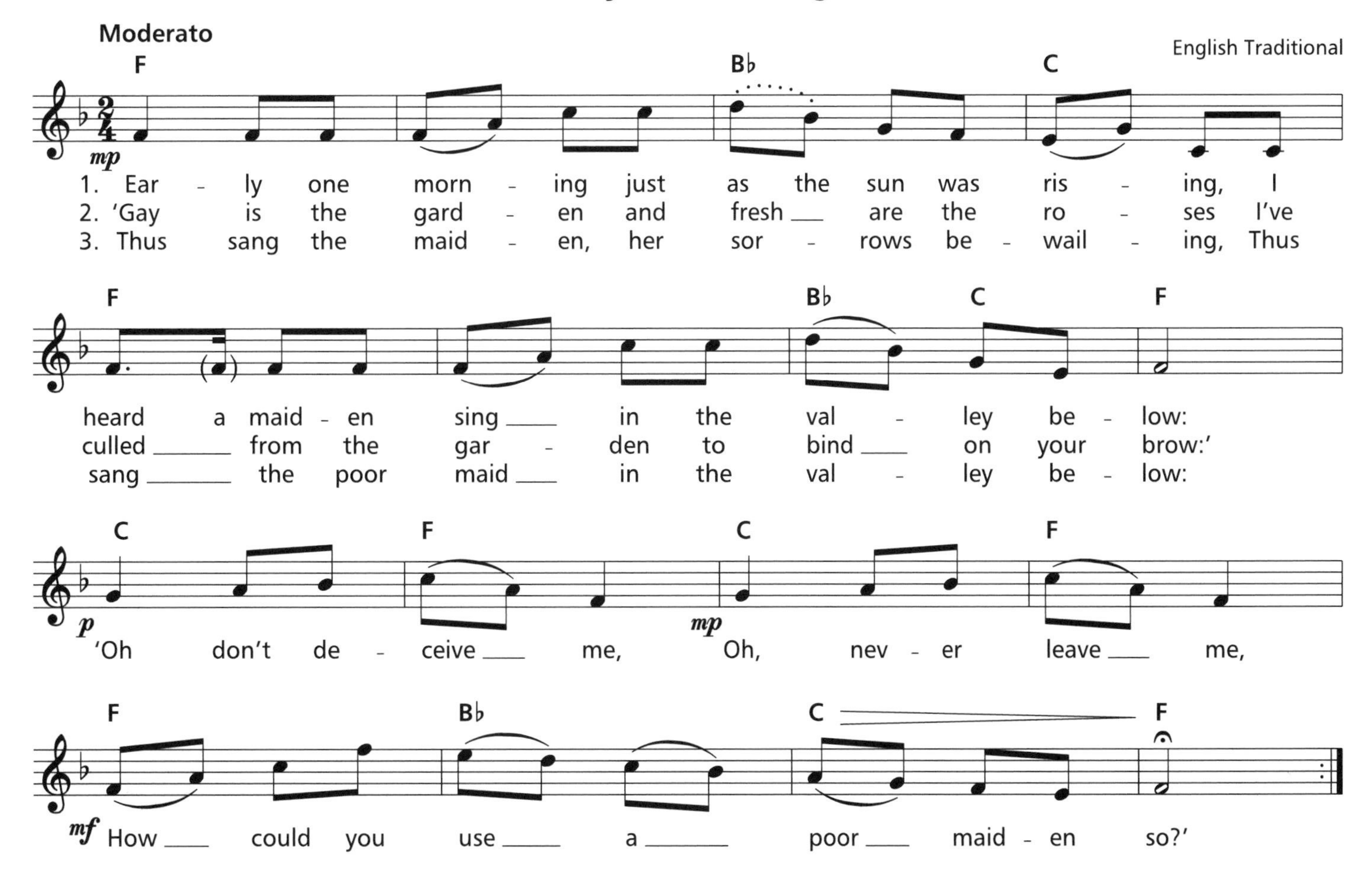

When you know this song well, sing the last four bars starting on different notes, as in these examples:

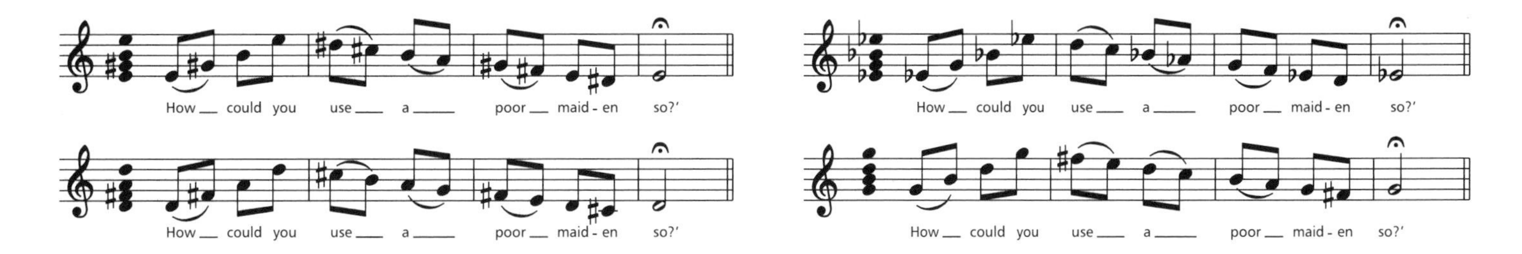

Compound duple time

Beat 1 Beat 2

Compound triple time

Beat 1 Beat 2 Beat 3

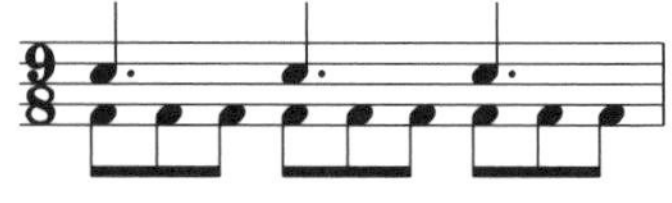

Compound times with dotted crotchet beats

London Birds starts in $\frac{6}{8}$ time, which is a 'compound' time. In compound times, main beats can be divided into *three* equal shorter notes. If there are two main beats to the bar, the time is called **compound duple time**. If there are three main beats to the bar, it is called **compound triple time**.

London Birds contains bars in both compound duple and compound triple times, using dotted crotchet beats. The last three bars are in $\frac{2}{4}$ time, and their crotchet beats are the same tempo as the previous dotted crotchet beats.

London Birds

Music by Geoffrey Shaw
Words by Margaret Shaw

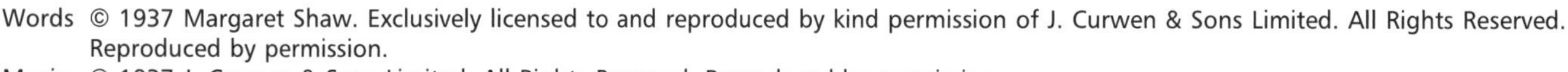
Words © 1937 Margaret Shaw. Exclusively licensed to and reproduced by kind permission of J. Curwen & Sons Limited. All Rights Reserved. Reproduced by permission.
Music © 1937 J. Curwen & Sons Limited. All Rights Reserved. Reproduced by permission.

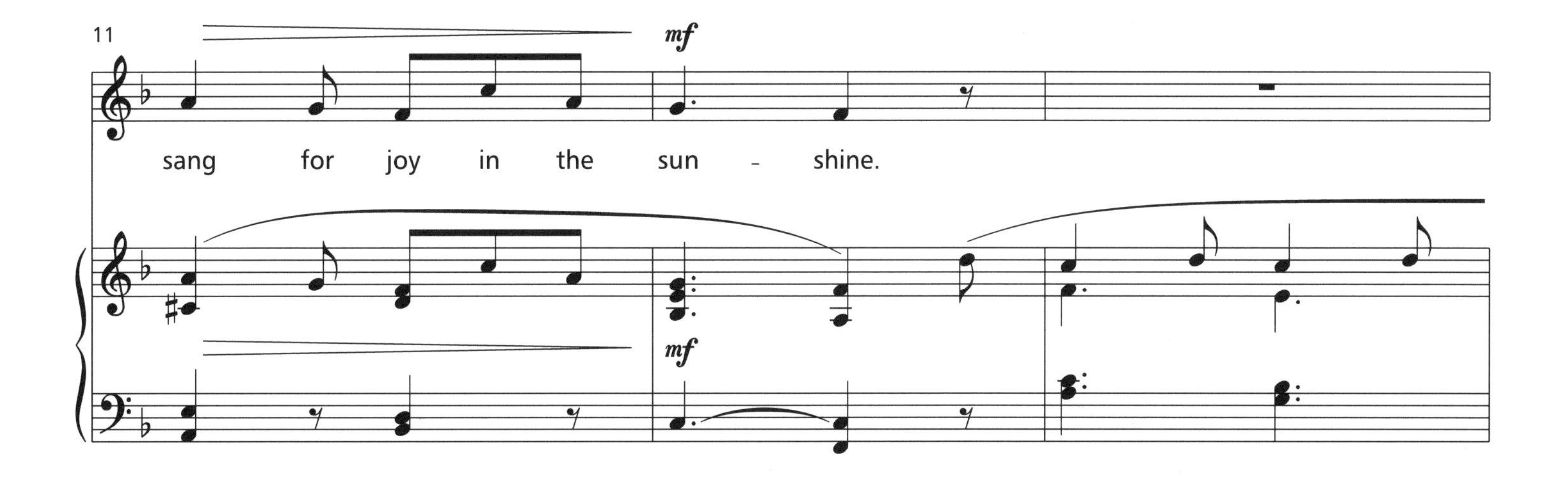
11
mf
sang for joy in the sun - shine.
mf

14
mf
I saw two ducks on the Ser - pen - tine,

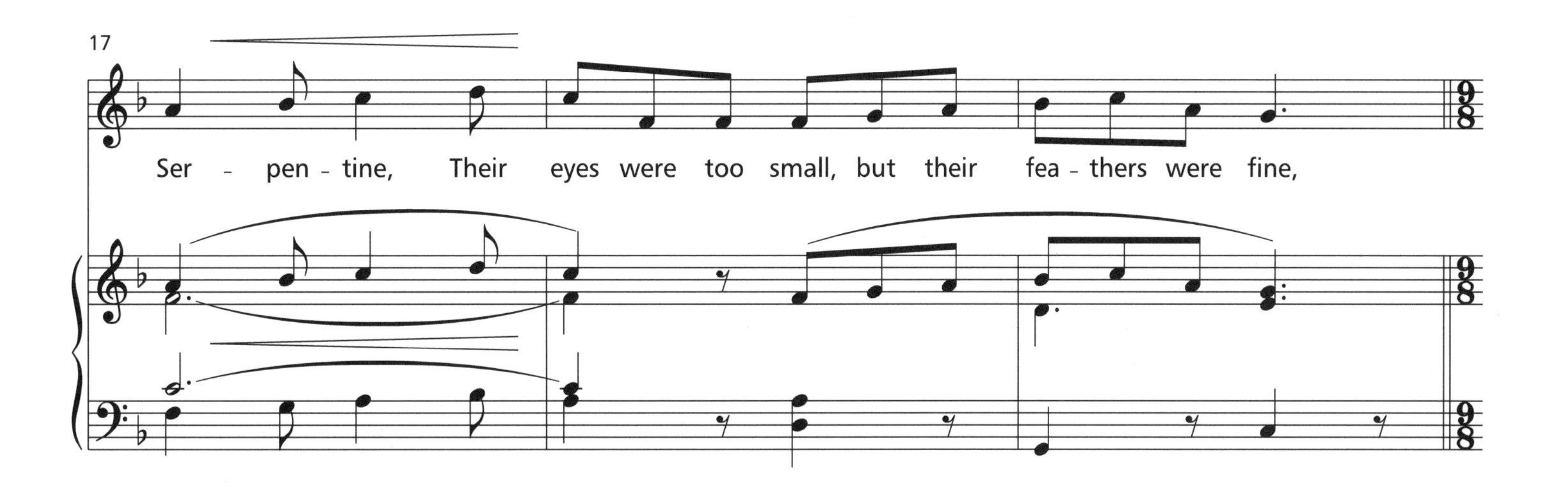
17
Ser - pen - tine, Their eyes were too small, but their fea - thers were fine,

20
f
fea - thers were fine, And they quacked for joy, quacked for joy,
f

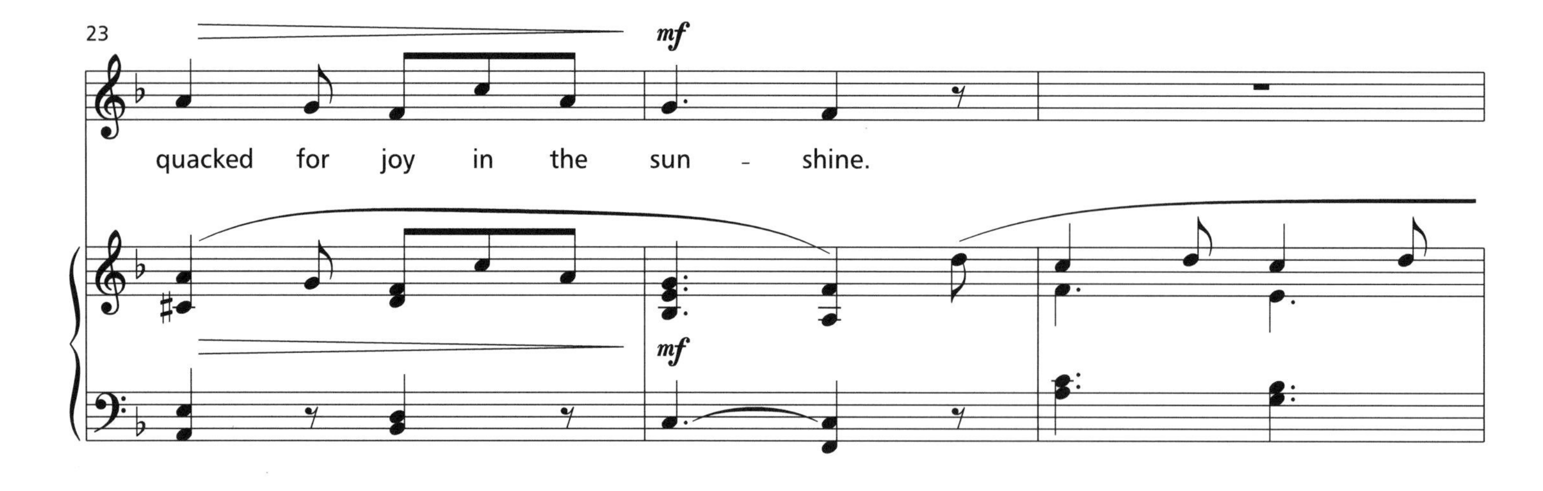
23
mf
quacked for joy in the sun - shine.
mf

26
mf
I saw three swans at Hamp - ton Court,

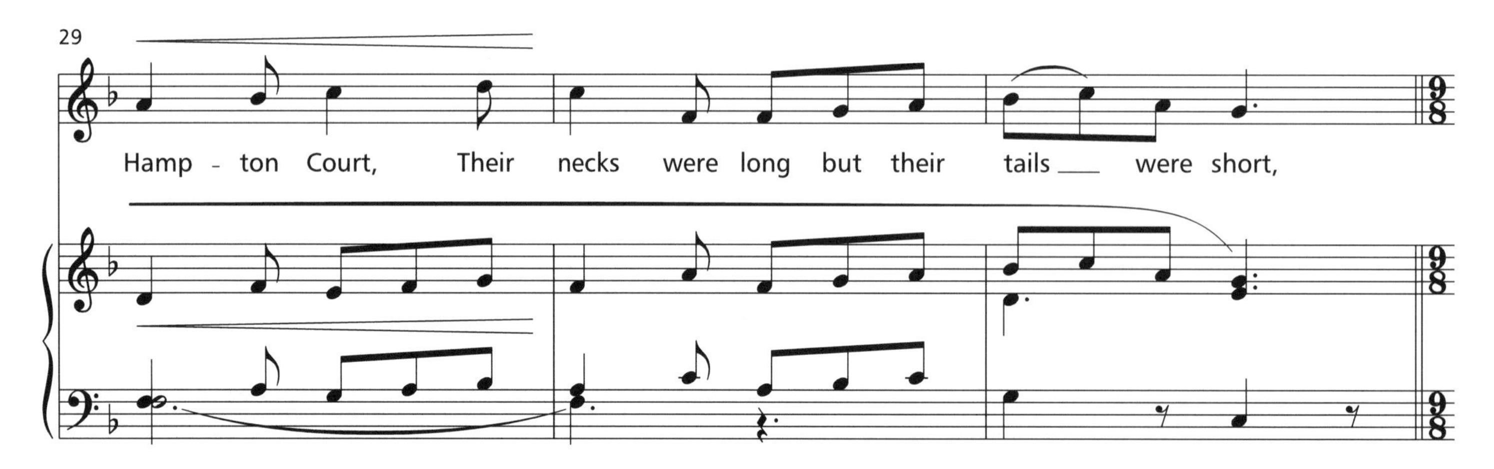
29
Hamp - ton Court, Their necks were long but their tails were short,

32
f
tails were short, And they swam ve - ry proud, swam ve - ry proud,
f

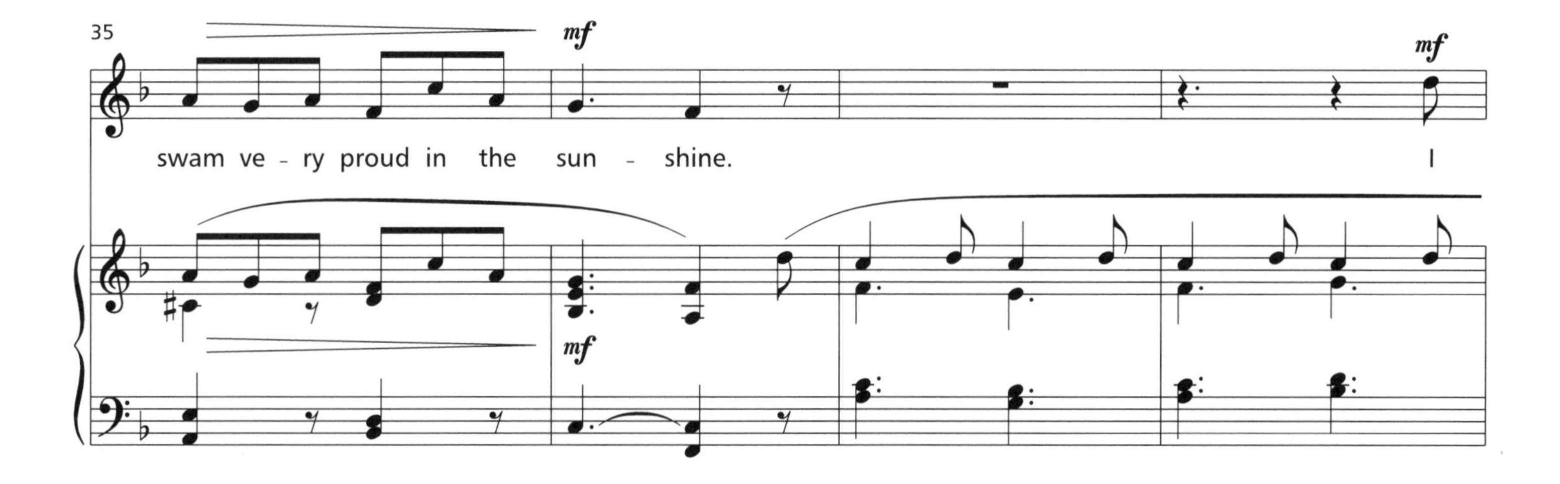
35
mf
swam ve - ry proud in the sun - shine.
I
mf

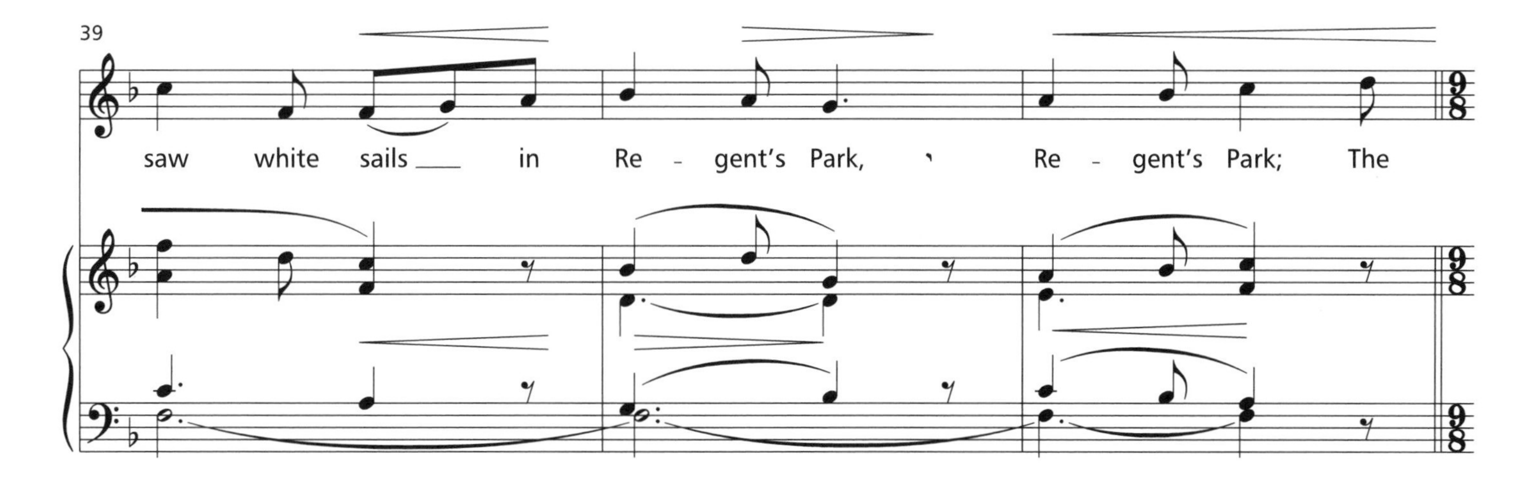
39
saw white sails in Re - gent's Park, Re - gent's Park; The

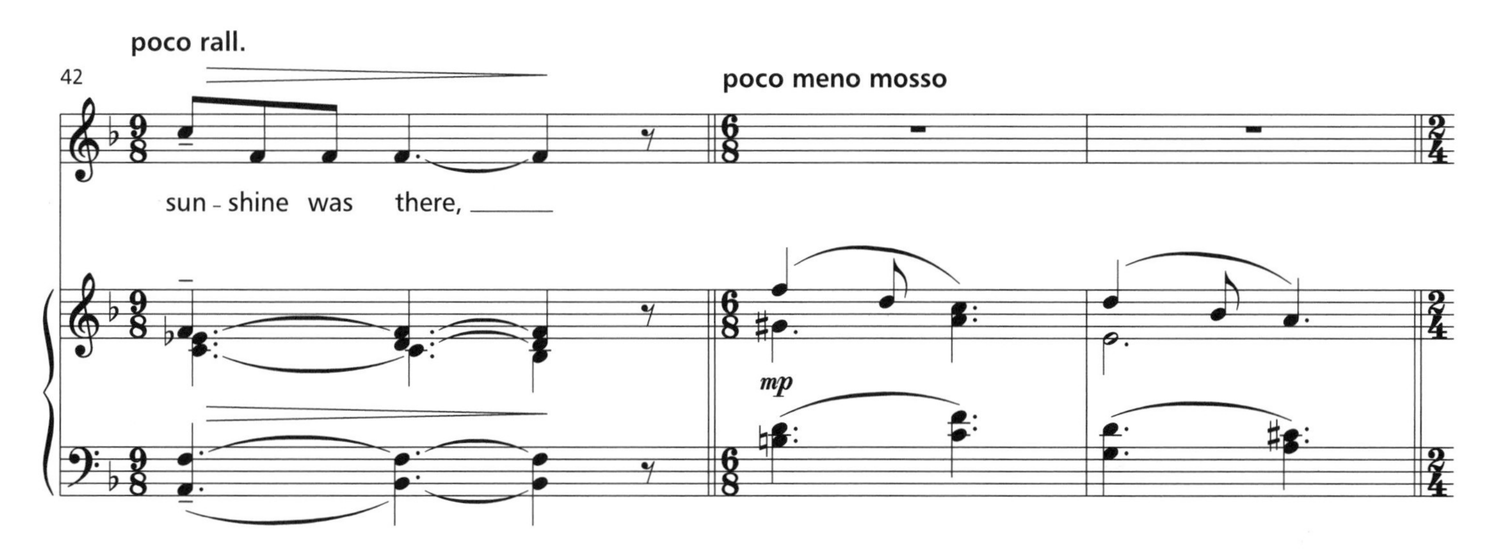
poco rall.
42
poco meno mosso
sun - shine was there,
mp

a tempo
45
mf
but I did - n't hear A lark.
mf

Part 3

Songs in G major

This Irish song is a set song for Grade 2.

Cockles And Mussels

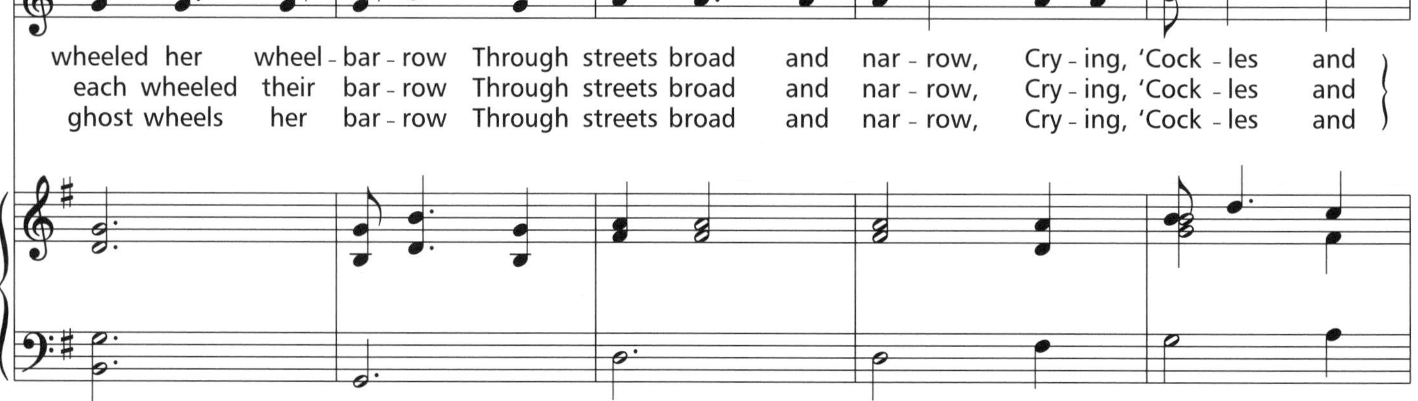

The British Grenadiers, like many quick marches, uses minim beats.

Notice that it starts on the last half-beat of the bar, not the first. Sometimes an opening like this is called an *upbeat* but the correct word is *anacrusis*.

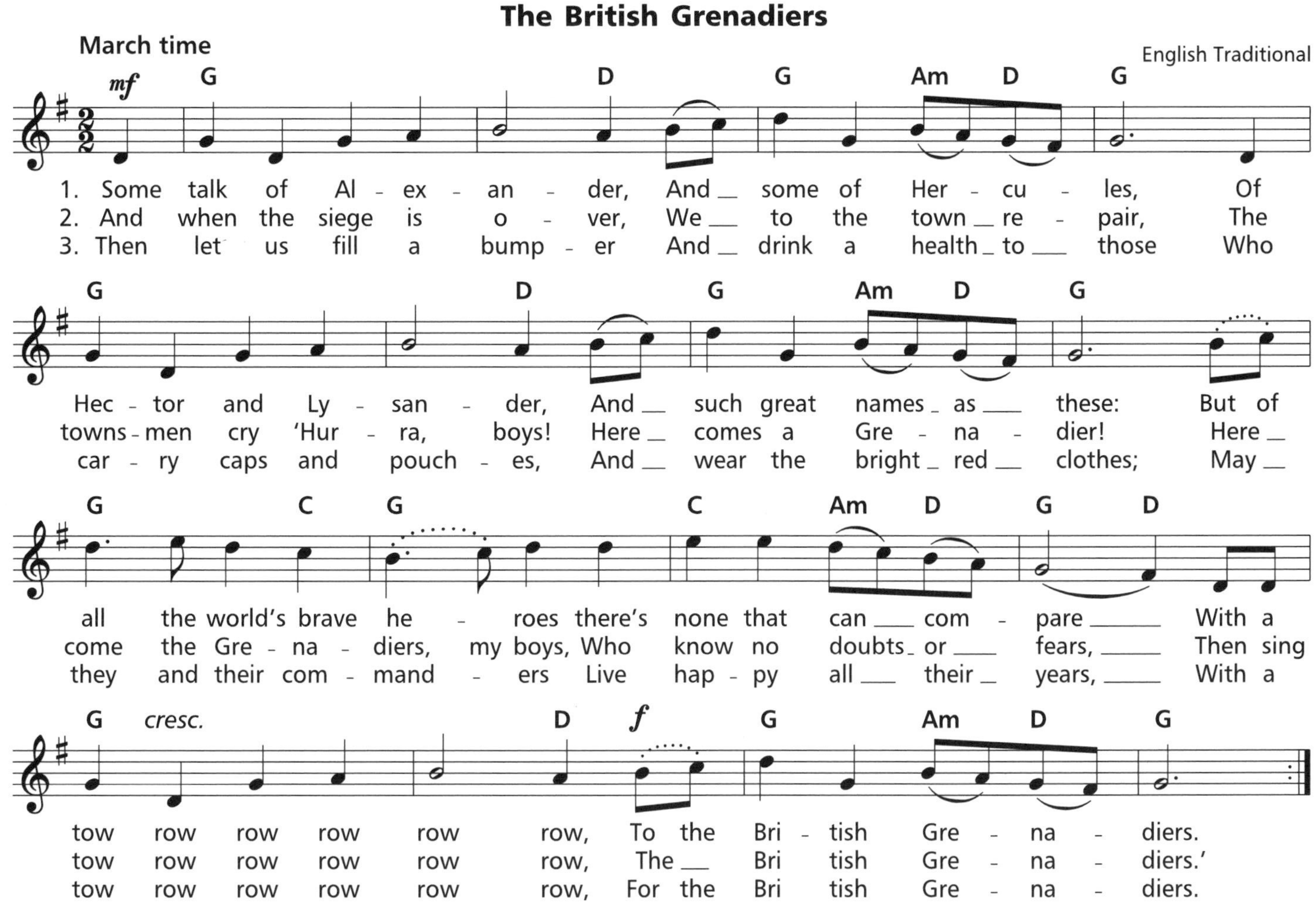

Irregular division of beats: triplets

Amazing Grace has some beats which are unusually divided.

It has three crotchet beats to the bar. Usually, crotchet beats are divided into halves (quavers), and quarters (semiquavers). In several bars here, though, a crotchet beat is divided into three quavers, each worth *one third* of a crotchet.

The subdivisions are called *triplets*. They are indicated by the figure *3*.

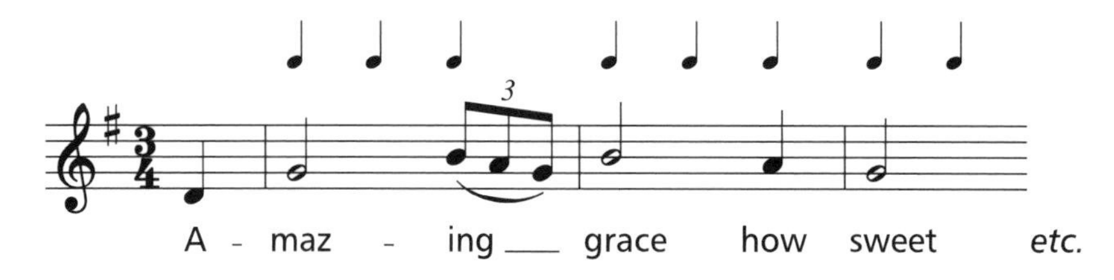

Amazing Grace is interesting for two reasons. First, though the song is written here in G major, it uses only five notes of the scale – G, A, B, D and E. Five-note scales are called *pentatonic* scales, and this one is known as the major pentatonic. Second, John Newton, the author of the words, was a captain of a slave ship, until he gradually came to realise that trading in slaves was evil.

Amazing Grace

4. The Lord has promised good to me,
   His word my hope secures;
   He will my shield and comfort be
   As long as life endures.

If you choose the next song for Grade 2, sing only two verses.

The Water Is Wide

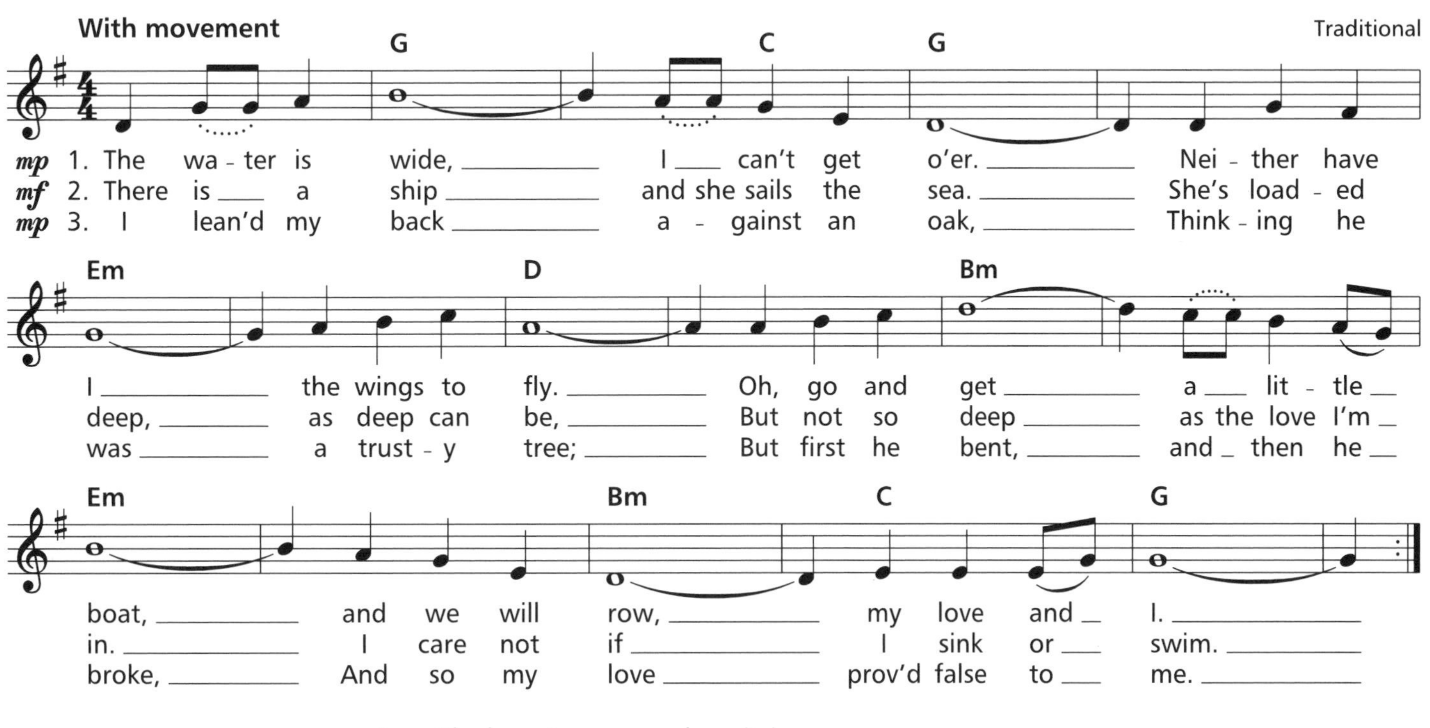

4. Oh, love is warm when it is new,
And love is sweet when it is true;
But love grows old and waxeth cold,
And fades away like morning dew.

I Got A Shoe

mp
2. I got a robe, you got a robe, *etc.*
Gonna shout all over God's heaven…

f
3. I got a song, you got a song, *etc.*
Gonna sing all over God's heaven…

Part 4

Songs in D and B flat majors

Two songs in D major

This well-known hymn is one of the set songs in List B.

Morning Has Broken

Traditional Gaelic Melody
Words by Eleanor Farjeon

Words by Eleanor Farjeon from THE CHILDREN'S BELLS published by Oxford University Press. Reproduced by permission.

Blow The Man Down on the next page needs a very strong rhythm. It was intended to help sailors in their work on deck.

Blow The Man Down

Two songs in B flat major

My Bonnie Lies Over The Ocean

This charming song by Schumann is in List B. If you sing it as an examination choice, omit verse 2. It is a quiet song, but you should vary the dynamics in your performance.

Butterfly
(Schmetterling)

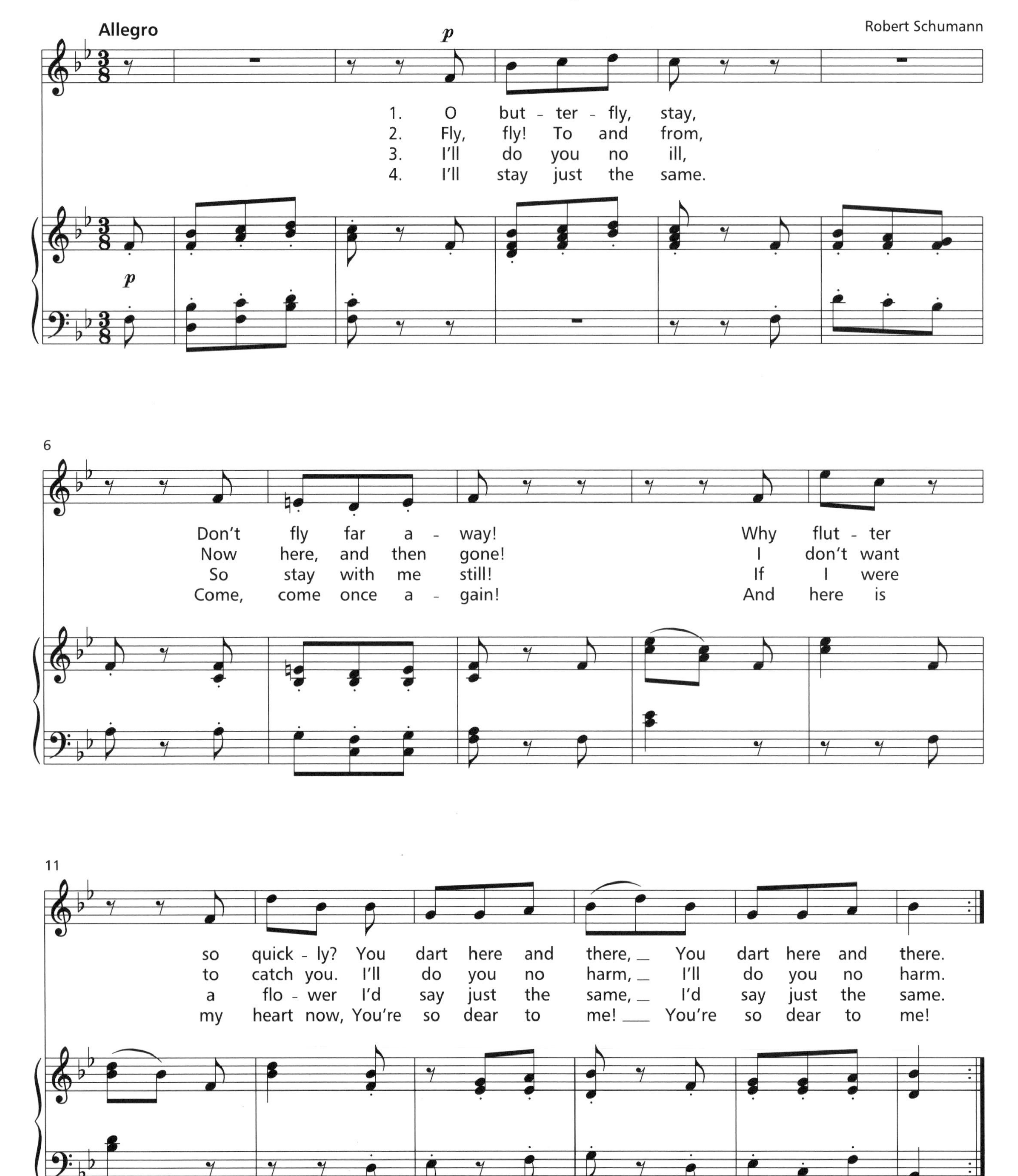

Part 5

Songs in E flat and A majors

He's Got The Whole World In His Hand

A major

A major also uses three black notes – C♯, F♯ and G♯.

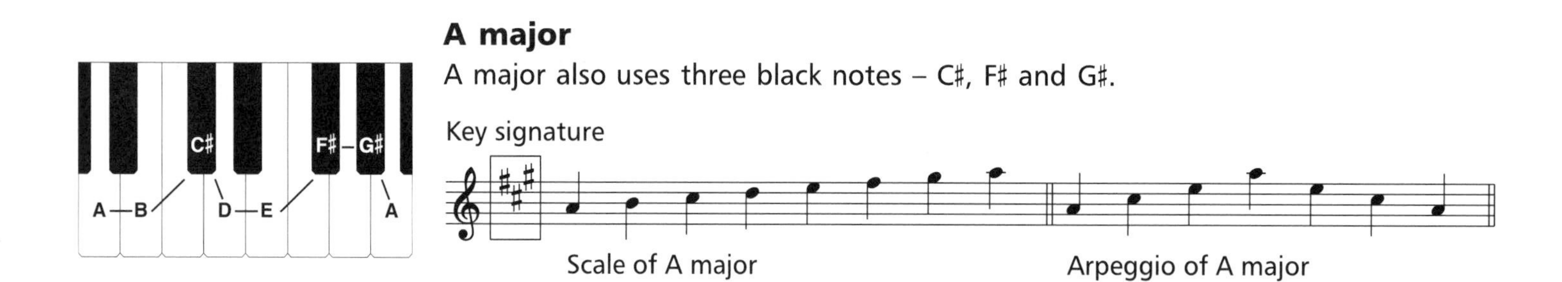

Scale of A major

Arpeggio of A major

The last song in this section needs particularly crisp articulation. Before you sing it, you may like to practise this exercise for consonants.

The Brave Old Duke Of York

Part 6

Beyond major keys

So far, songs have been in major keys. However, you will often meet songs in minor keys, or which use other types of scale-like modes. You will learn more about minor scales and modes later in your musical studies, but here are some songs to sing now.

A minor

A minor has the same key signature as C major (no sharps or flats), but as in all minor scales notes 6 and/or 7 may be raised by a semitone. In the case of A minor this means that note 6 can be F or F♯, and note 7 can be G or G♯.

G minor

G minor has the same key signature as B♭ major (B♭ and E♭). Notes 6 and/or 7 may be raised by a semitone. In the case of G minor this means that note 6 can be E♭ or E♮, and note 7 can be F or F♯.

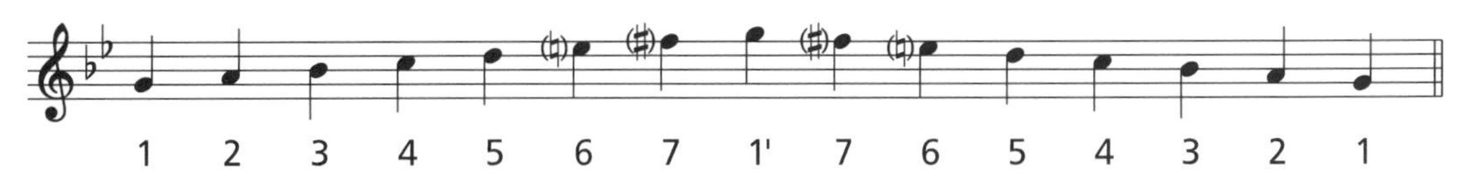

Sing this beautiful carol with well contrasted dynamics. Verse two can be sung loudly, and the final refrain should be very quiet.

Notice how the refrain and the verses end on B♮ above a chord of G major. This type of major-key ending to a minor-key piece is known as a *tierce de Picardie*. Make sure the major third of the scale (B♮) is bright and well in tune.

Coventry Carol

Reprinted by permission of A. R. Mowbray & Co Ltd.

E minor

E minor has the same key signature as G major (F♯), and notes 6 and/or 7 may be raised by a semitone. In the case of E minor this means that note 6 can be C or C♯, and note 7 can be D or D♯.

Greensleeves

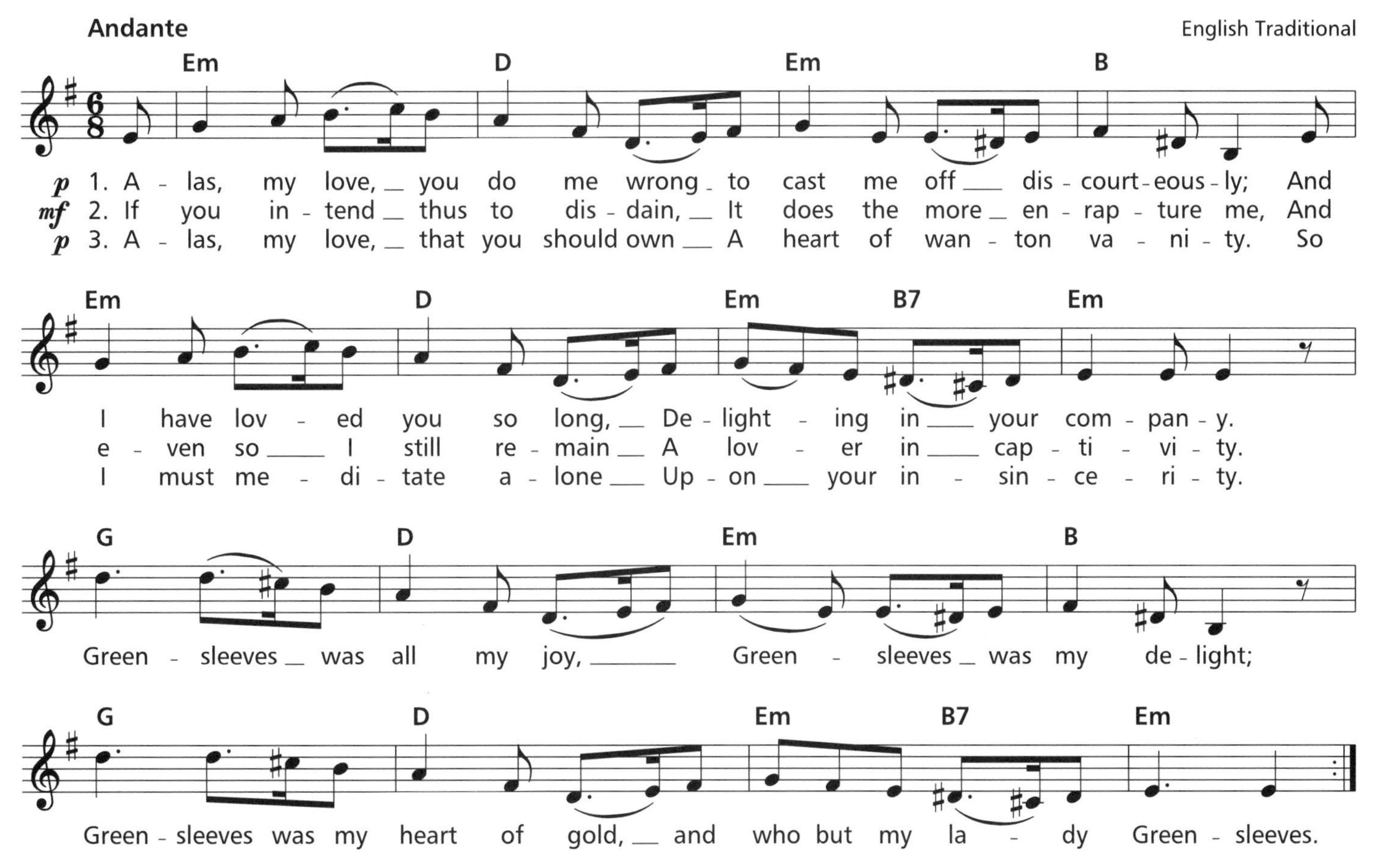

Stance and presentation

Stand as still as you can when performing songs. Keep your head up, and 'take in' the listeners in your look. Remember that in accompanied songs the piano part is important too, so stay still until the piano part ends. Look at the audience as much as you can.

If you need to use printed music when practising, hold it in both hands at a comfortable level – not too high.

The Little Spanish Town, on the next page, has a strongly marked Spanish rhythm in the accompaniment and the quavers in the voice part will need crisp articulation of consonants. Notice that although the song is written in $\frac{4}{4}$ time, there are bars in $\frac{2}{4}$ time near the end of each verse.

You will see that the vocal part in the last eleven bars has the direction *Lower part optional* written above it. If you are singing the song by yourself, you must sing the upper vocal part in these bars.

The Little Spanish Town

Words and music by Peter Jenkyns

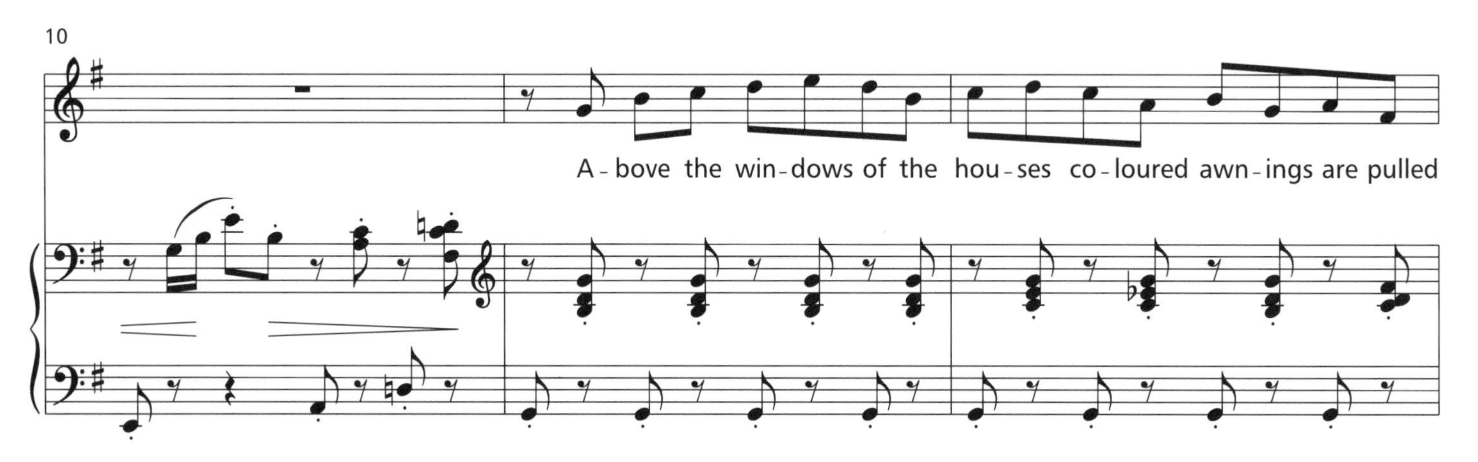

© Copyright 1963 Novello & Company Limited. All Rights Reserved. Reproduced by permission.

13
mp
down.
And some-where mu-sic starts to
p

16
mur-mur in the lit-tle Span-ish town.

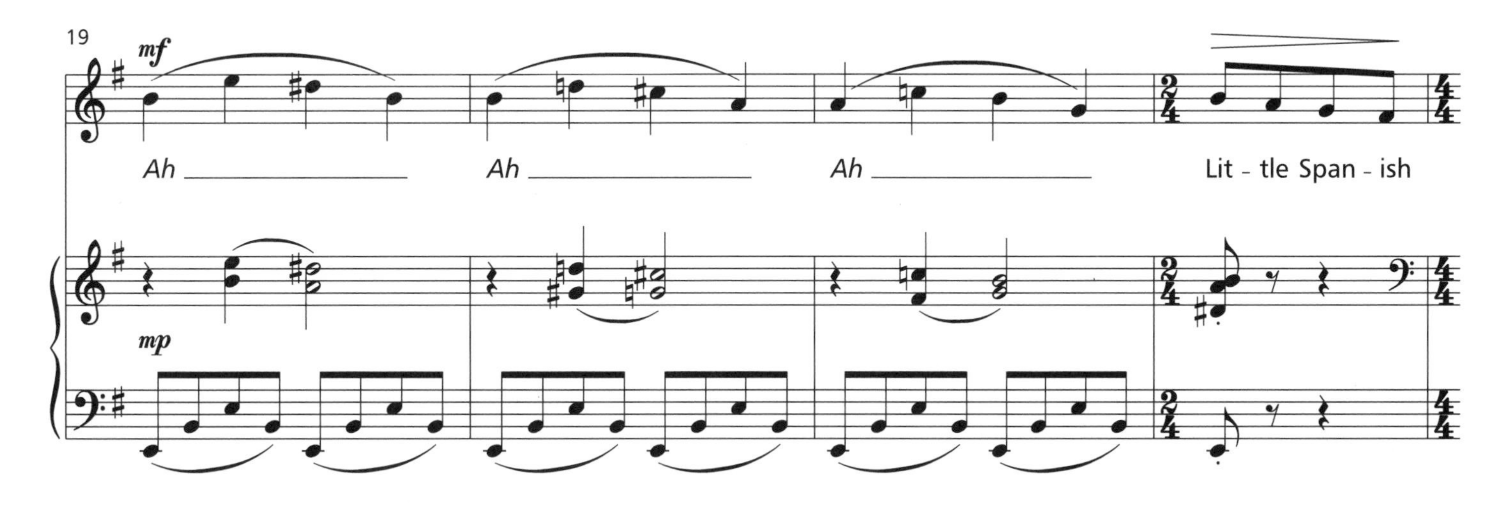
19
mf
Ah
Ah
Ah
Lit-tle Span-ish
mp

23
p
mf
town.
A hol-i-day for danc-ing
pp
mp

26
and for drink - ing wine has just be - gun,
29
The dark - eyed sen - o - ri - tas click - ing heels and sway - ing in the sun;
32
A sun whose glow - ing warmth and gol - den light are al - ways there to

35
mp
crown
A - no - ther day of joy and
p

38
laugh - ter in the lit - tle Span - ish town.

Lower part optional
41
mf
Ah
Ah
Ah
Lit - tle Span - ish
mp

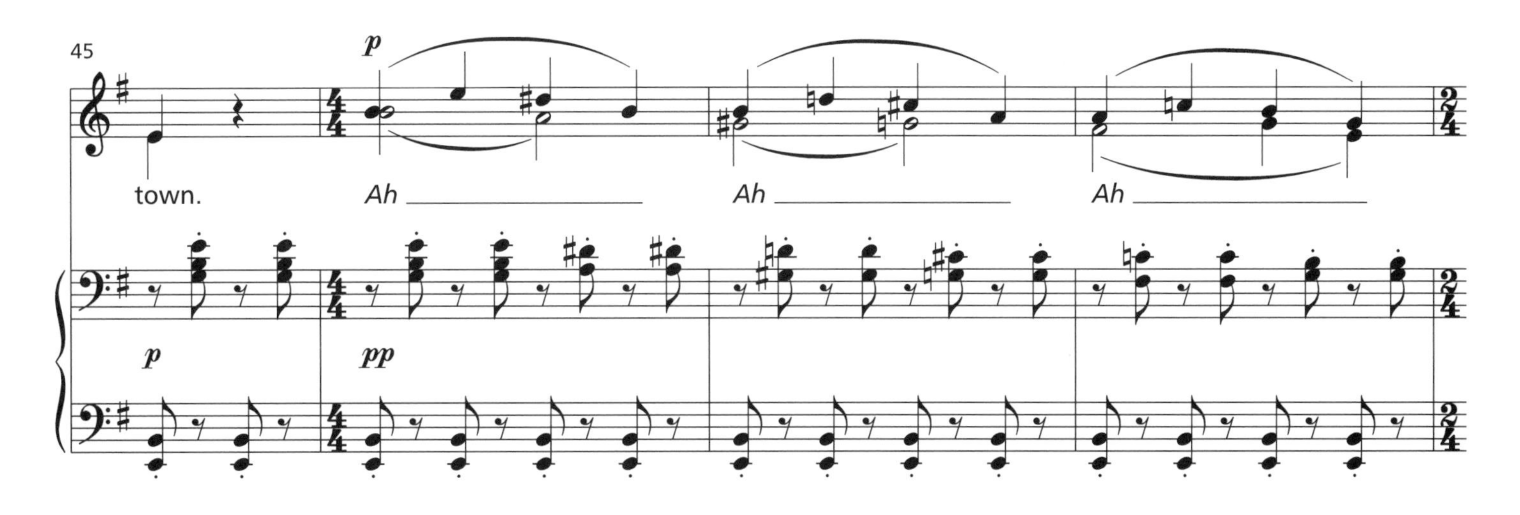
45
p
town.
Ah
Ah
Ah
p
pp

49
pp dim.
ppp
Lit - tle Span - ish
town.
dim.
ppp

The Oak And The Ash

Modes

The last two songs in this section use types of scales called modes. *Scarborough Fair* uses the scale D–E–F–G–A–B–C–D. This is known as the Dorian mode.

Traditional Border melody
Words by Thomas Pringle

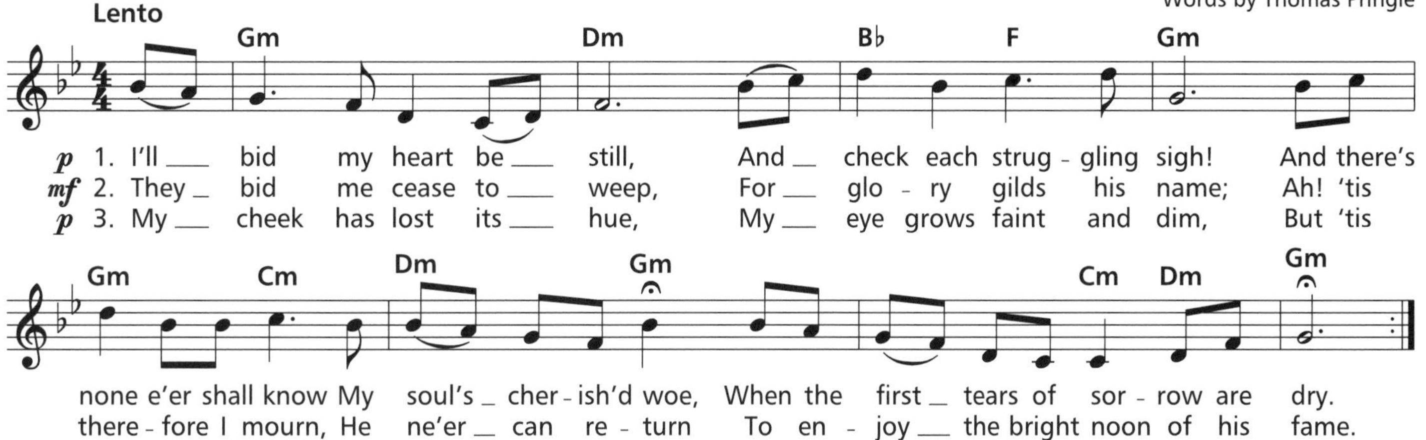

Part 7

Singing with other people

Singing by yourself, or with an accompanist, is fun. But you can also get enjoyment by singing with other people, either in small groups or in a large choir.

The songs in this book can be sung by groups of any number of singers singing the melodic line. Often, though, songs are written with several vocal lines (or 'parts'). Look at the last eleven bars of *The Little Spanish Town* on page 29. The upper vocal part must be sung by one singer or group of singers. The lower vocal part may be sung by another singer, or group of singers. Try to sing these bars in two parts, with a friend or group of friends.

Here is another song which can be sung by two groups of people:

I Ain't Gonna Grieve My Lord No More

2. You can't get to heav'n in a rocking chair,
'Cause the Lord don't want no lazybones dere.

3. You can't get to heav'n on roller skates,
You'll roll right by those pearly gates.

4. If you get to heav'n before I do,
Just bore a hole and pull me through.

Canons and rounds

In this piece, voice 1 starts the melody in bar 1. In bar 2, voice 2 starts to sing the same melody, imitating voice 1 but a bar later. This type of music is called a *canon*.

Tallis's Canon

Now sing this simple round. Three voices, or groups of voices, are needed. Everyone should first sing the whole round through several times. Then voice 1 should sing the round through. When voice 1 reaches the end of the first line, voice 2 starts at the beginning. When voice 2 has reached the end of the first line, voice 3 starts. When a voice has finished, it may start singing the round again. A leader is needed, to bring the round to an end, and to vary dynamics.

Sing Together

When you sing with other people, you must know your own part thoroughly. Then you will be able sing accurately, and at the same time be able to listen carefully to the other parts. Find your own starting note from the given key note, or from notes sung in other parts. This takes practice, but it is very satisfying. Here are some more rounds:

White Sand And Grey Sand

Come, Follow Me

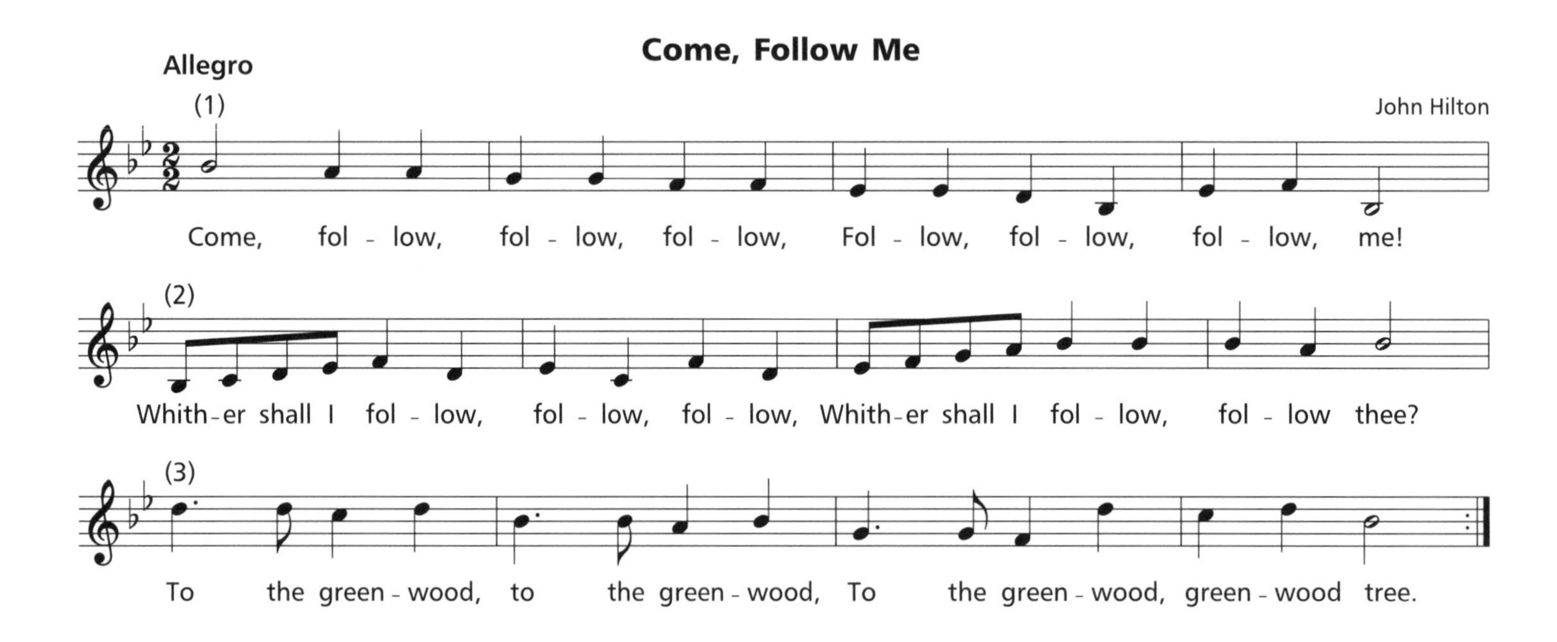

This last round is for four voices and is in D minor – be careful of the C♯.

Ah, Poor Bird

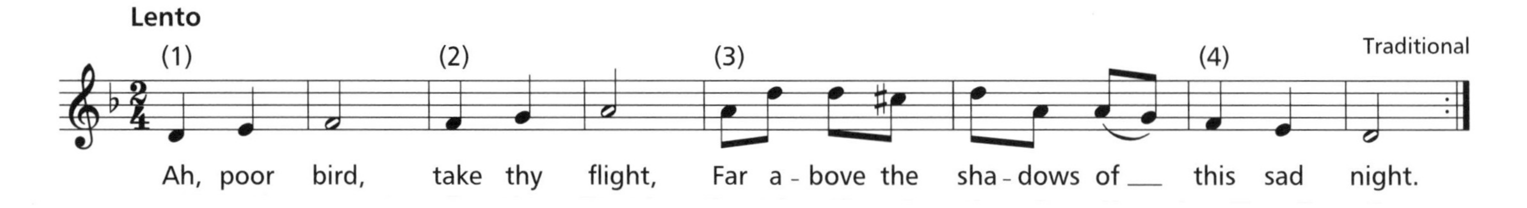

Part 8

Singing at sight

Singing at sight is difficult at first. Here is an example of the type of test you might have to sing at sight:

In examinations, you will be played the key chord and key note, and then given half a minute to prepare the test. You will be played the key chord and key note again, just before you have to sing the piece. When practising, though, take as much time as is necessary to master the steps listed below – you will get faster with experience.

When you sing tests in exams, you may sing notes to the printed words, *or* to any vowel, *or* to sol-fa names. When practising, though, it is better to sing the words, as they help you understand the mood of the song.

- Work out the rhythm. At first, write in the counting. Clap the rhythm of the introduction, then the words.
- Decide what key the piece is in, and on which note of the key it starts. See if your starting note is played by the piano in the introduction.
- Most of the melodic movement will be stepwise, but there may be jumps. If you find a jump, work out its interval.
- Look at the dynamics and any expression marks, and be sure to include them.
- Sing the song slowly at first. When confident, sing it at its suggested tempo. In the exam, the accompaniment will be played by the examiner, who will therefore set the speed for you.

Using this approach, prepare and sing the song above, then continue with the other examples on the next pages.

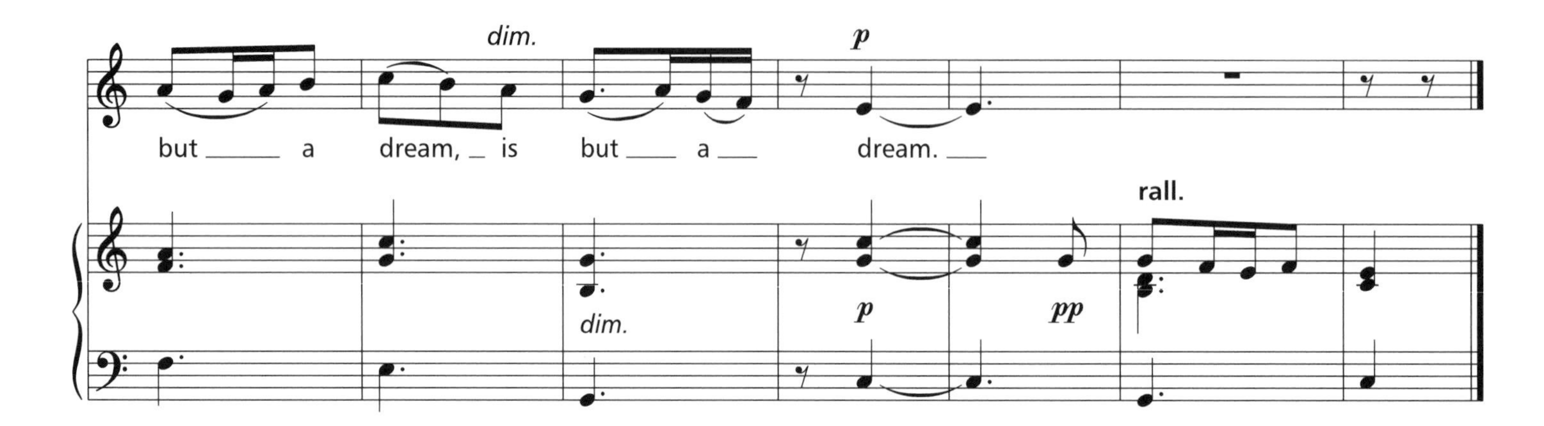

Count particularly carefully in this test – the rhythm is sometimes unexpected.

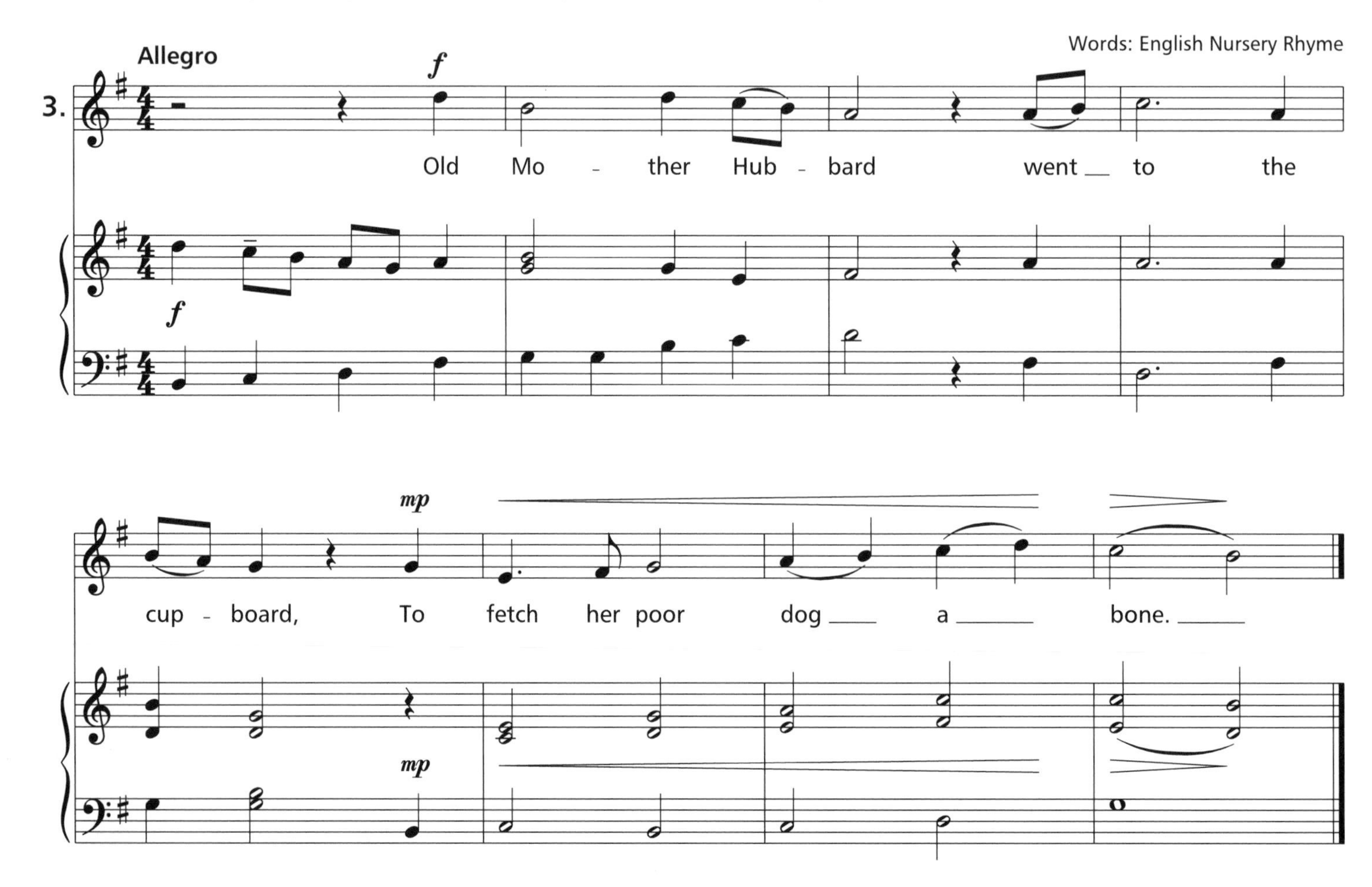

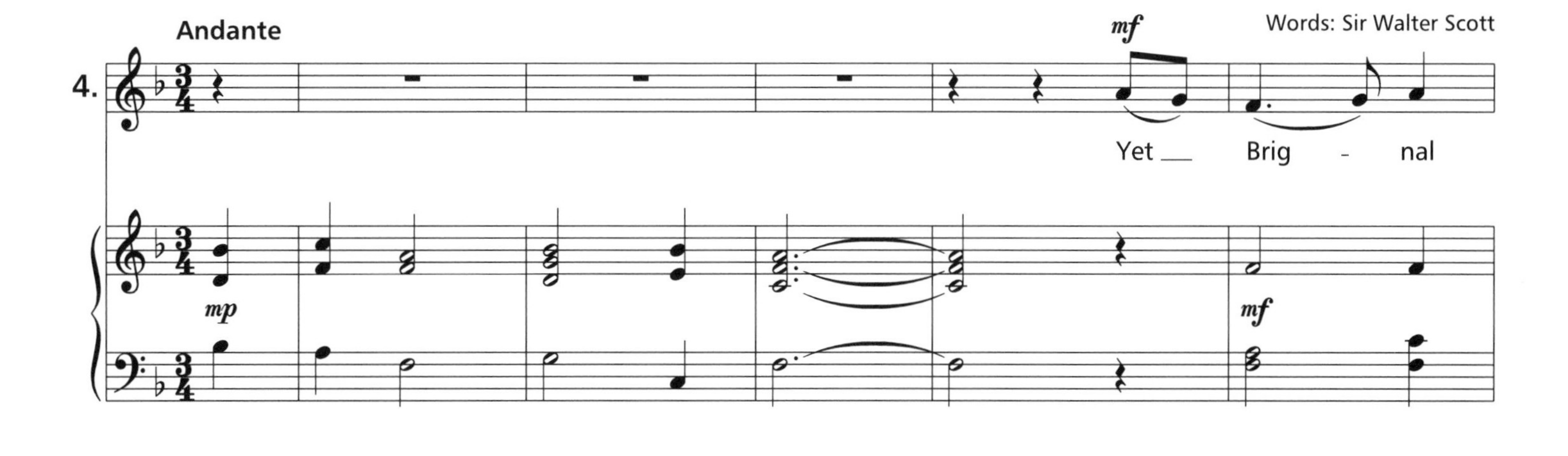
Andante
Words: Sir Walter Scott
4.
mf
Yet __ Brig - nal
mp
mf

banks are fresh and fair, And Gre - ta woods __ are

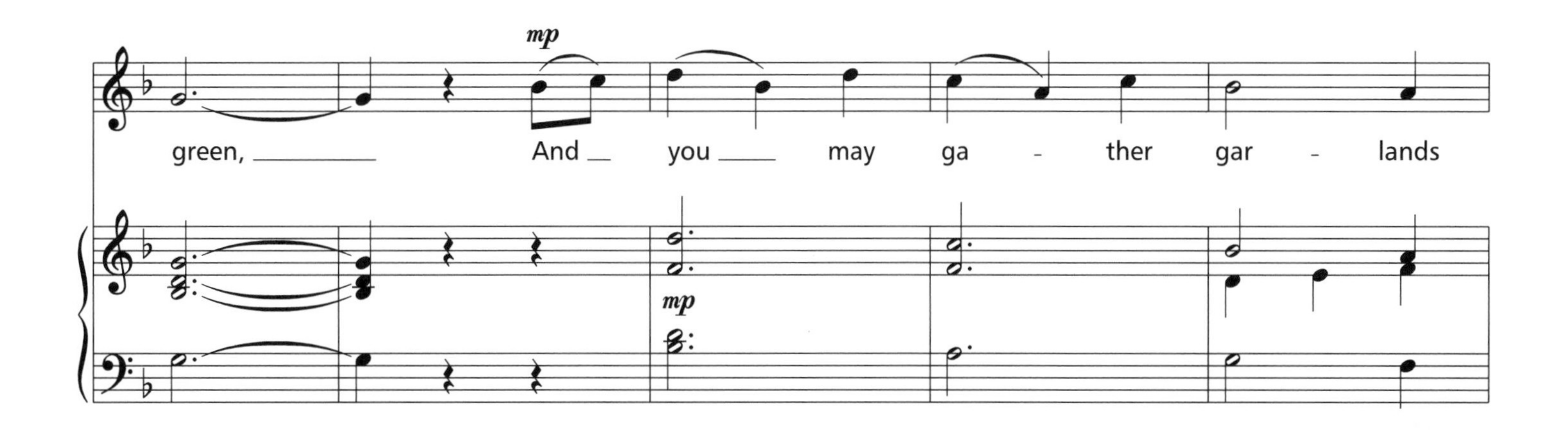
mp
green, ________ And __ you ____ may ga - ther gar - lands
mp

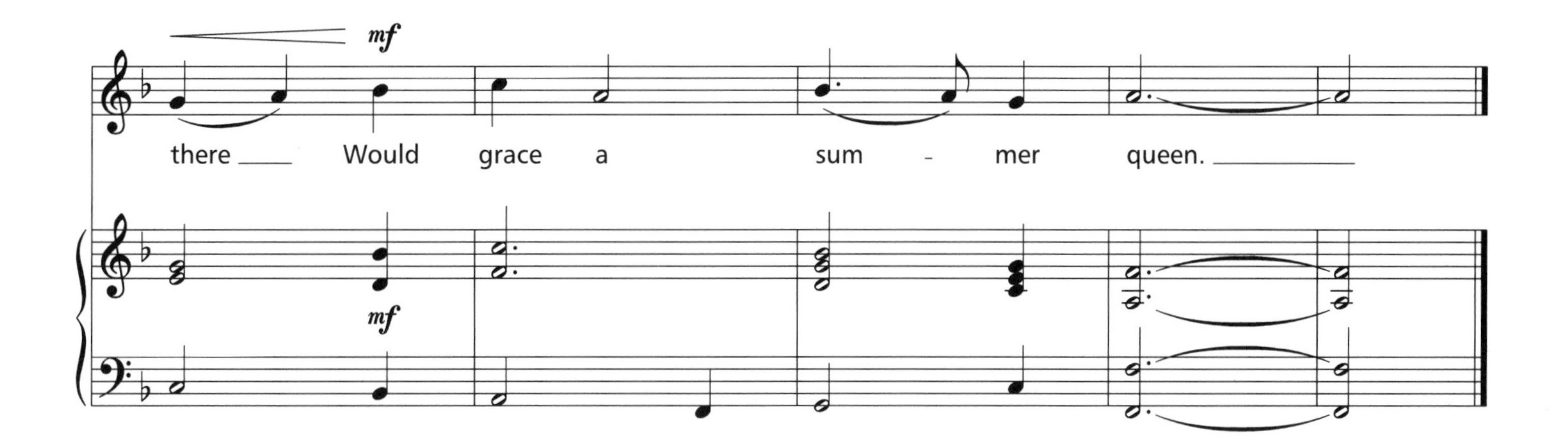
mf
there ___ Would grace a sum - mer queen. __________
mf

Words: Lewis Carroll

Lento
Words: George Herbert
6.
p
Sweet day, so cool, so calm, so
bright, The bri - - dal of the earth and
sky, The dew shall weep thy fall to -
- night, For thou must die.

Words: W. S. Gilbert
Allegro
7.
Oh,
I am a cook and a cap - tain bold, And the mate of the Nan - cy
brig,
And a bo' - sun tight, and a
mid - ship - mite, And the crew of the cap - tain's gig!

Tempo di valse
8.
Words: Edward Lear
f
Far and few, ___
f

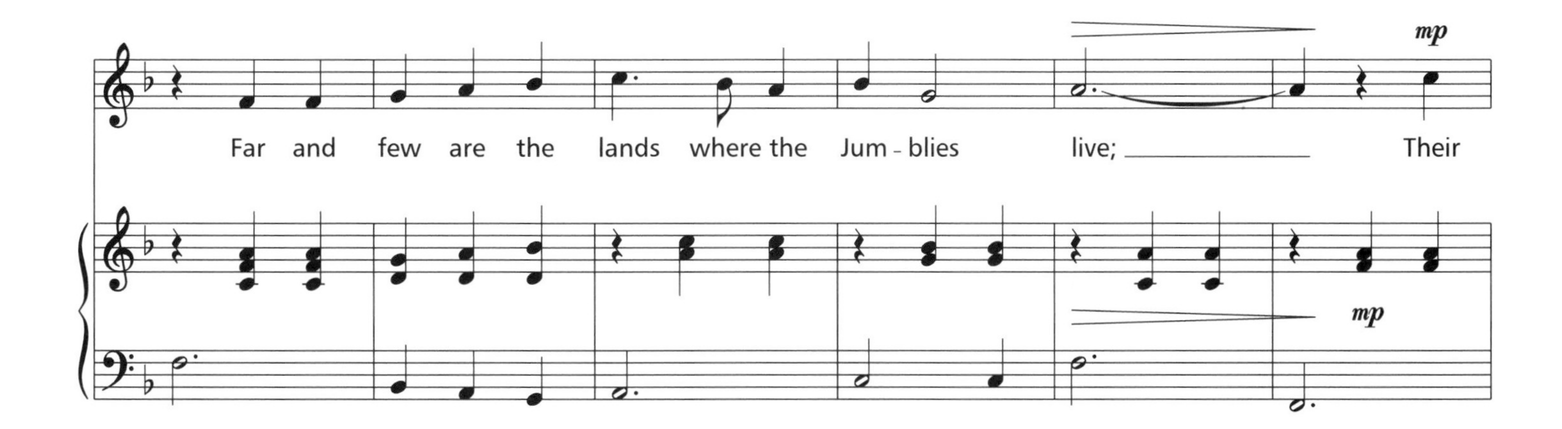
mp
Far and few are the lands where the Jum - blies live; ___ Their
mp

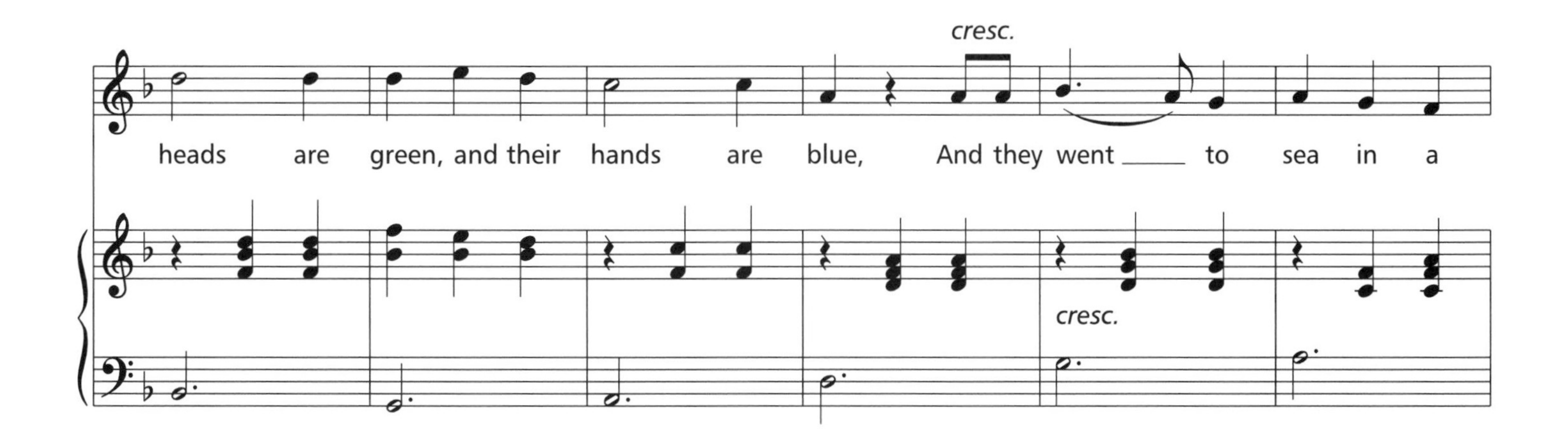
cresc.
heads are green, and their hands are blue, And they went ___ to sea in a
cresc.

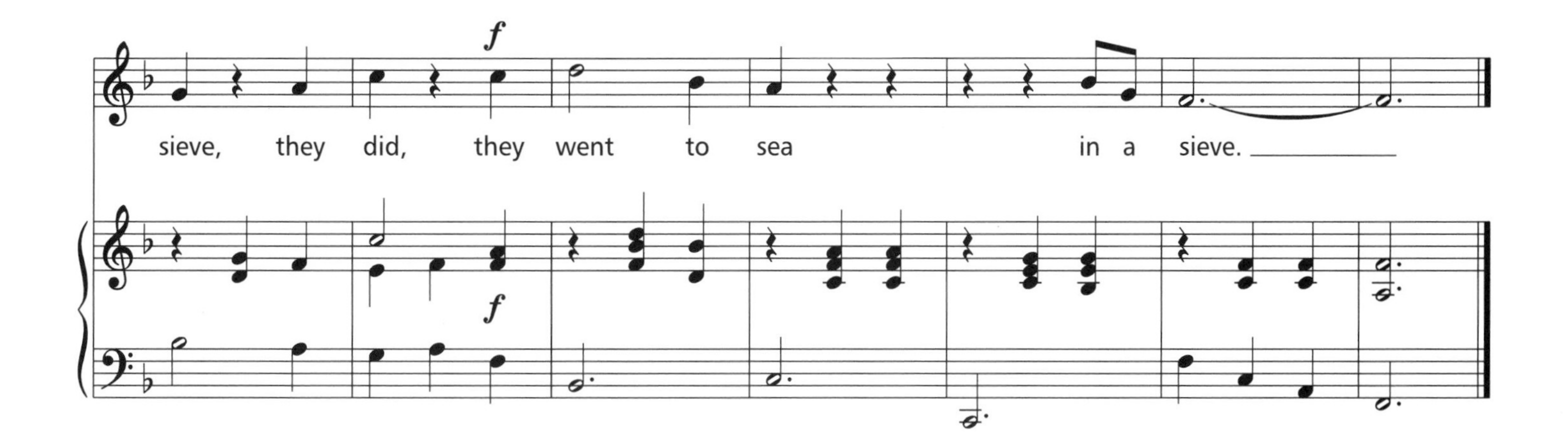
f
sieve, they did, they went to sea in a sieve. ___
f

Moderato
Words: William Shakespeare
9.
Love, whose month is ev - er May, Spied a bloss - om

pass - ing fair
Play - ing, play - ing in the wan - ton air.

Words: William Blake
Lento
10.
The sun des - cen - ding in the west, The eve - ning star does
shine: The birds are sil - ent in their nest, And I must seek for mine.

English Traditional
arranged by Cecil J. Sharp
Allegro moderato
11.
There was a far - mer had three sons, Three sons to him were born, And he came home right in the mid - dle of the night, And he turned them out of doors, and he turned them out of doors, And he came home right in the mid - dle of the night, And he turned them out of doors.

In this test, the rhythm is sometimes syncopated.

Count carefully, and listen to the introduction which will help you with the rhythm of the vocal line.

Musical terms and signs

Tempo

a tempo	in tempo
adagio	slow, leisurely
allegro	fairly fast
allegretto	fairly fast, but less than *allegro*
andante	moderate walking pace
lento	slow
moderato	at a moderate speed

Changes to Tempo

accelerando	getting faster gradually
rallentando (rall.)	getting slower gradually
ritardando (rit.)	getting slower gradually
ritenuto (rit.)	holding back

Manner of Performance

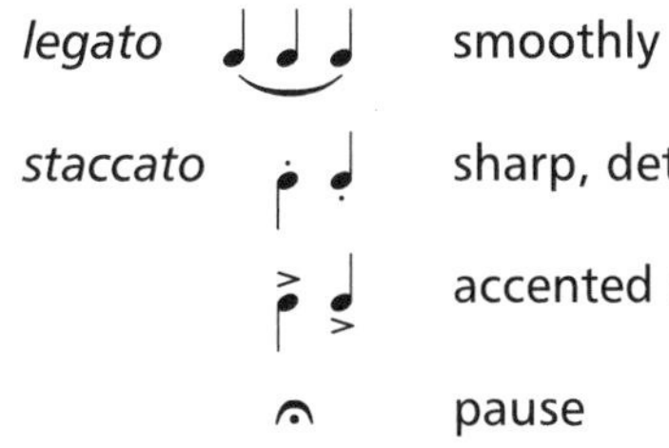

legato	smoothly
staccato	sharp, detached
	accented notes
	pause

Dynamics

forte	***f***	loud
fortissimo	***ff***	very loud
mezzoforte	***mf***	moderately loud
mezzopiano	***mp***	moderately quiet
piano	***p***	quiet
pianissimo	***pp***	very quiet

Changes to Dynamics

crescendo (cresc.)	<	getting gradually louder
decrescendo (decresc.)		getting gradually quieter
diminuendo (dim.)	>	getting gradually quieter

Performance Instructions

𝄆	𝄇	repeat the music between these bar lines
da capo	*D.C.*	repeat from the beginning
dal segno	*D.S.*	repeat from the 𝄋 sign
Fine		end
♩=60	A speed of 60 crotchets per minute.	

Use the staves below to write down the openings of tunes you choose to help you remember intervals (see page 5).

The author wishes to record his thanks to

Lesley Rutherford of Bosworth/Music Sales for expert editing;
Paul Terry of Musonix, for advice and admirable typesetting;
Diana Turnbull for German translations, and for many hours of help with text and proof-reading.

Index of songs

Also in this series:

Aural Time!

Practice Tests for ABRSM and other exams

Like most musical skills, aural awareness needs regular training and practice. Aural work should be part of every lesson; teachers will find these books useful as supplementary material for practice in lessons, and ideal as preparation for all instrumental exams. The piano accompaniments to all tests have been kept simple.

Grade 1 BOE004796
Grade 2 BOE004797
Grade 3 BOE004798
Grade 4 BOE004799
Grade 5 BOE004800 Pupil's Book BOE004909 (Grades 4/5)
Grade 6 BOE004921 Pupil's Book BOE004924 CD of 99 examples BOE004921CD
Grade 7 BOE004922 Pupil's Book BOE004931 CD of 99 examples BOE004922CD
Grade 8 BOE004923 Pupil's Book BOE004929

Theory Time!

Step-by-step instruction for ABRSM and other exams

The principles of theory covered in the clearest possible way for people new to music. Ideal preparation for exams or as part of a general music education. Explains everything you need to know at each level, checking understanding with frequent tests. Answers are provided.

Grade 1 BOE004868
Grade 2 BOE004869
Grade 3 BOE004870
Grade 4 BOE004907
Grade 5 BOE004908

Scale Time!

A step-by-step approach to scales, arpeggios and broken chords

Scales are essential to the development of a fluent piano technique. The gradual approach in this book towards learning scales – with plenty of hints and tips – is ideal for exams as well as for general technique.

Grade 1 BOE004992
Grade 2 BOE004996
Grade 3 BOE004997
Grade 4 BOE004998
Grade 5 BOE005001
Grade 6 BOE005010

Bosworth
8-9 Frith Street, London W1V 5TZ
Exclusive distributors:
Music Sales Limited, Newmarket Road, Bury St Edmunds, Suffolk IP33 3YB

Printed by Printwise (Haverhill) Limited, Suffolk 7/09 (170294)